This book
belongs to

....

make
believe
ideas

The Princess and the Pea

Key sound r-blends spellings:
br, cr, dr, fr, gr, pr, tr
Secondary sounds: in, ng, ss

Written by Rosie Greening
Illustrated by Clare Fennell

Reading with phonics

How to use this book

The **Reading with phonics** series helps you to have fun with your child and to support their learning of phonics and reading. It is aimed at children who have learned the letter sounds and are building confidence in their reading.

Each title in the series focuses on a different key sound or blend of sounds. The entertaining retelling of the story repeats this sound frequently, and the different spellings for the sound or blend of sounds are highlighted in red type. The first activity at the back of the book provides practice in reading and using words containing the sound. This title looks at a key consonant blend group, where two or more consonants are blended together, but each sound may be heard in the blend. The key group of consonant blends for **The Princess and the Pea** is the r-blend.

Start by reading the story to your child, asking them to join in with the refrain in bold. Next, encourage them to read the story with you. Give them a hand to decode tricky words.

Now look at the activity pages at the back of the book. These are intended for you and your child to enjoy together. Most are not activities to complete in pencil or pen, but by reading and talking or pointing.

The **Key sound** pages focus on one sound or on a group of consonant blends. Encourage your child to read the different letter groups and complete the activity, so they become more aware of the variety of spellings there are for the same sound or for the group of consonant blends.

The **Letters together** pages look at three pairs or groups of letters and at the sounds they make as they work together. Help your child to read the words and trace the route on the word maps.

Rhyme is used a lot in these retellings. Whatever stage your child has reached in their learning of phonics, it is always good practice for them to listen carefully for sounds and find words that rhyme. The pages on **Rhyming words** take six words from the story and ask children to read and find other words that rhyme with them.

The **Key words** pages focus on a number of key words that occur regularly but can nonetheless be challenging. Many of these words are not sounded out following the rules of phonics and the easiest thing is for children to learn them by sight, so that they do not worry about decoding them. These pages encourage children to retell the story, practising key words as they do so.

The **Picture dictionary** page asks children to focus closely on nine words from the story. Encourage children to look carefully at each word, cover it with their hand, write it on a separate piece of paper, and finally, check it!

Do not complete all the activities at once – doing one each time you read will ensure that your child continues to enjoy the stories and the time you are spending together. **Have fun!**

Prince Frank lived with his mum, the queen, but got under her feet.

He played
the drums...

dropped lots
of crumbs...

... and always stole her seat!

The prince annoys the queen a lot.
He sits down in her favourite spot!

The queen felt grumpy as can be.
"I want some peace!" she said.
"Let's try to find another place
where you can live instead."

6

Frank just groaned, but then cried out,
"I'll make a deal with you.
I'll move out if you help me find
a princess who is true!"

The prince annoys the queen a lot.
The grumpy queen grows red and hot.

The queen found Frank some pretty girls:
each gracious through and through.
But Frank was such a fussy prince
that not one girl would do!

"You're far too tall."

"You're way too small."

"Your grubby
ears stick out."

"Your nose is big."

"You've dropped your wig."

"You smell like Brussels sprouts!"

The prince annoys the queen a lot.
He doesn't like the girls one jot!

The queen cried to the prince one day,
"You're too hard to impress!"
But Frank just grinned and said again,
"I want a true princess!"

10

But then, one freezing, drizzly night,
a girl knocked at the door.
Her dress was drenched, and as she walked
it dripped across the floor.

The prince annoys the queen a lot.
The pretty girl drips on the spot.

"My name is Princess Grace," she said.
"Could I please stay the night?"
The queen thought, "This could be the one,"
and so she cried, "Alright!"

But Frank was far more doubtful,
so he soon dreamt up a plot.
"I'll play a trick to see if she's
a royal girl or not."

The prince annoys the queen a lot.
He'll come up with a crafty plot.

The crafty prince crept off upstairs
to make young Grace a bed,
but stacked up fifty mattresses
and blankets there instead.

14

And then he tucked a bright-green pea
beneath the groaning pile.
"A true princess will feel the pea,"
the prince thought with a smile.

**The prince annoys the queen a lot.
He'll see if Grace is true or not.**

When pretty Grace came in to sleep,
she stared up at the bed.
Prince Frank gave her a stepladder.
"Goodnight, sweet dreams!" he said.

The prince annoys the queen a lot.
It's time for bed, so off they trot!

When morning came, young Grace crept down
to have some bread and tea.
But when the queen asked how she'd slept,
the girl cried, "Dreadfully!"

"I didn't sleep at all last night,"
said Grace, looking confused.
"My bed had something hard inside
that made me very bruised!"

The prince annoys the queen a lot.
Grace shows Frank the bruise she got.

Cried Frank with glee, "You felt the pea,
so you're a true princess!"
The queen asked Grace to live with Frank,
and prayed that she'd say yes.

"I will, but promise me one thing,"
the grinning princess said.
"Please stop your son from putting peas
inside my comfy bed!"

The prince annoys the queen a lot.
Grace agrees to tie the knot.

The prince and princess moved away,
and soon the pair were wed.
The queen was happy as could be –
"At last, some peace!" she said.

The prince annoys the queen a lot.
A peaceful home is what she's got!

Key sound

The **r-blends** are **br**, **cr**, **dr**, **fr**, **gr**, **pr** and **tr**. Practise these sounds by looking at the words in the flowers and using them to make sentences. Can you use each word in a different sentence?

crab
cry
cross

bring brick
brown break
branch

dry drip
dream
drum dress

pretty
prize
prison

fry
friend
frog

grass
grapes
grin

tree
trumpet
train
true

Letters together

Look at these pairs of letters and say the sounds they make.

in **ng** **ss**

Follow the words containing in to find the prince.

in

ring

happy

grin

bed

thing

nose

inside

door

prince

Follow the words that contain ng to find the grinning queen.

ng

freezing

putting

young

long

then

smell

something

grinning

Follow the words that contain ss to find a real princess.

peace

clever

ss

Kiss

queen

dress

across

night

mattress

princess

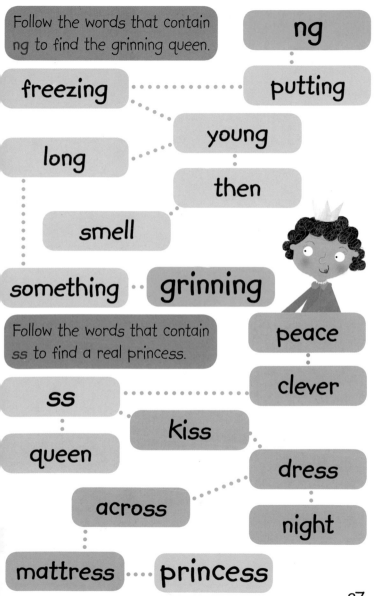

Rhyming words

Read and say the words in the flowers, and then point to other words that rhyme with them.

blue	**true**	you
queen		crown

guess	**dress**	blanket
pile		yes

she	**pea**	King
free		see

live   **long**   strong

plot   wrong

in   **grin**   clever

found   win

mum   peace

thing

sing   king

Now choose a word and make up a rhyming chant!

Let's **see** if **she** will feel the **pea**!

Key words

Many common words can be tricky to sound out.
Practise them by reading these sentences about
the story. Now make more sentences using
other key words from around the border.

Prince Frank annoyed
his **mum**, the queen.

The queen asked
Frank to move **out**.

She found
some pretty girls
for Frank.

But Frank
wanted to marry
a true princess.

Grace **said** she
was a princess.

not • your • mum • his • he

• said • very • a • for • had • made • put • off • on •

Prince Frank decided to test **her**.

He **put** a pea inside Grace's bed.

Grace **was** a princess because she felt the pea.

The queen **asked** Grace to live with Frank.

"At last, **some** peace!" said the queen.

her • saw • in • but • make • out • called • look • by • about • up • you • they • asked

old • see • like • into • some • with • was • to

Picture dictionary

Look carefully at the pictures and the words.
Now cover the words, one at a time.
Can you remember how to write them?

bed

bruise

crumbs

drenched

drums

pea

princess

queen

stepladder